100% Unofficial Minecrafters Unite:

A CENTUM BOOK 978-1-913865-80-1
Published in Great Britain by Centum Books Ltd
This edition published 2021
1 3 5 7 9 10 8 6 4 2

We have produced this "100% Unofficial Minecrafters Unite" book
independently from Mojang Synergies AB, the owner of the MINECRAFT®
registered trade marks. To be completely clear, this book has not
been authorised, approved, licensed, sanctioned or sponsored by
Mojang Synergies AB. Mojang Synergies AB owns all rights
to MINECRAFT products and trademarks.

Text and design © Centum Books | Images © Shutterstock & © Istock

Produced by The Wonderful Ideas Project LTD
with Fiona Munro (Words) and Lisa Robb (Art).
Special consultants: Bobby Chance, Will Shepherd, Jamie & Harry Dockray
Additional illustrations: Caroline Martin

Centum Books Ltd, 20 Devon Square,
Newton Abbot, Devon, TQ12 2HR, UK
9/10 Fenian St, Dublin 2, D02 RX24, Ireland
books@centumbooksltd.co.uk

CENTUM BOOKS Limited Reg. No 07641486

A CIP catalogue record for this book is
available from the British Library.

Printed in China

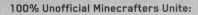

CONTENTS

TOP TEN TIPS

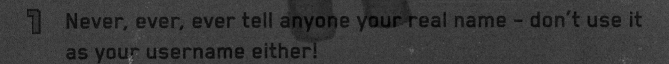

1. Never, ever, ever tell anyone your real name – don't use it as your username either!

2. Don't tell anyone your age, school or address

3. Don't give out any other personal info – about you, your friends or your family

4. Your passwords are there to keep you safe – don't share them with anyone (except your parents or carers)

5. There are lots of websites where you need to be over 13 to create an account. ALWAYS ask your parents or carers for permission before registering for websites

6. If something doesn't feel right, it probably isn't right. Always share worries with your parents or carers

7. Always be kind online. If someone is mean to you, tell your parents or carers straightaway. Remember it's always supposed to be fun!

8. Take lots of breaks from gaming and the screen, the best players know that rests and real-life skills make them better gamers!

9. It is better to play in shared spaces or close to your parents or carers

10. Remember you don't need to spend money to have fun online

WELCOME TO ME!

Use this blank template to create your character's look.

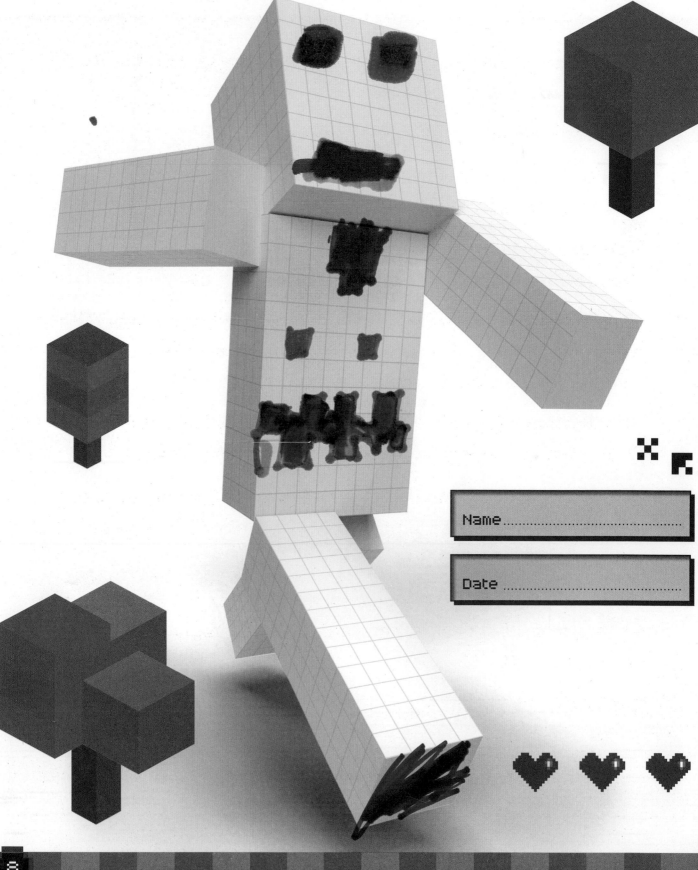

Name..

Date..

FAVOURITE HAIR COLOUR

black

FAVOURITE HAIRSTYLE

Spike

FAVOURITE JACKET

MineCraft

FAVOURITE TEE SHIRT

Minecra
FA

FAVOURITE TROUSERS

Minecraft

FAVOURITE FOOTWEAR

sceting

LOOT AND TREASURE GUIDE

SHIPWRECKS

THERE ARE THREE TYPES OF CHEST IN A SHIPWRECK:

MAP CHESTS contain paper, feathers, books, buried treasure maps, empty maps, compasses and clocks.

SUPPLY CHESTS contain wheat, rotten flesh, paper, carrot, coal, potato, poisonous potato, gunpowder, pumpkin, enchanted leather clothes (all pieces) and TNT.

TREASURE CHESTS contain iron nuggets, iron ingots, lapis lazuli, emeralds, gold nuggets, gold ingots, bottles o' enchanting and diamonds.

ORE-SOME QUIZ!

Test your deep, deep knowledge of the underground adventuring worlds.

1 What should you take with you to store valuables?

a   An ore bath
b   An ender chest
c   A block bag

2 Which of these is NOT a type of mining?

a   Cave mining
b   Strip mining
c   Over mining

3 Caves are typically found below what layer?

a   54
b   3
c   10

4 Which of these cannot naturally spawn underground?

a   Skeleton
b   Cow

5 Which of these ores is the most rare?

a   Redstone
b   Lapis lazuli

BOOM

BOOM BOOM

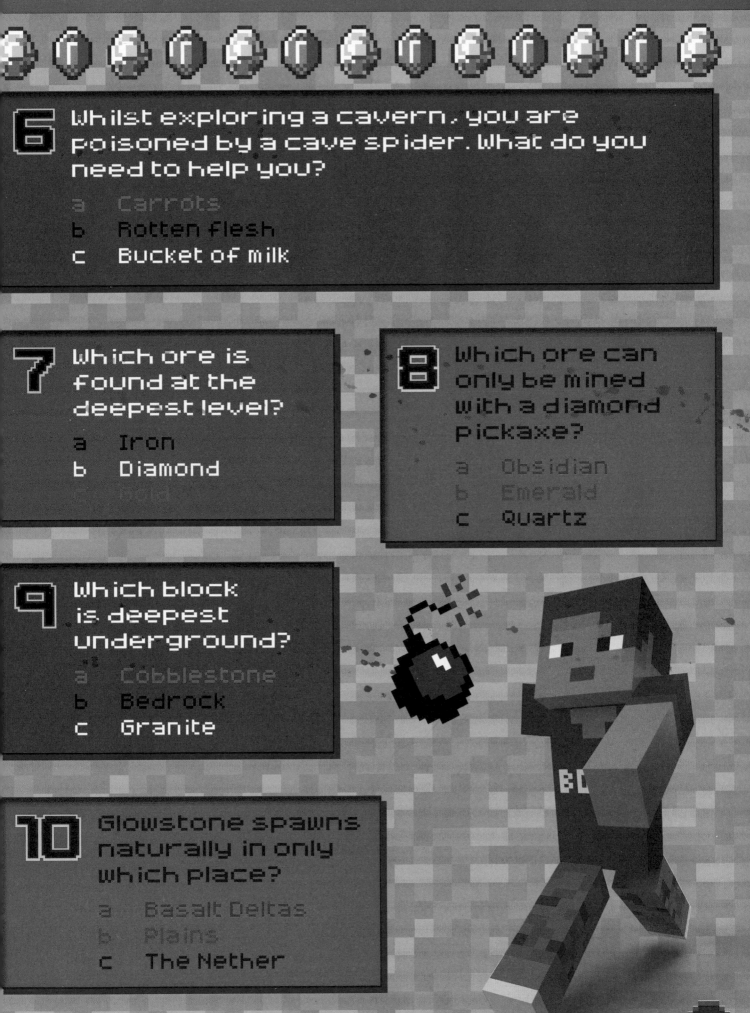

6 Whilst exploring a cavern, you are poisoned by a cave spider. What do you need to help you?

a Carrots
b Rotten flesh
c Bucket of milk

7 Which ore is found at the deepest level?

a Iron
b Diamond
c Gold

8 Which ore can only be mined with a diamond pickaxe?

a Obsidian
b Emerald
c Quartz

9 Which block is deepest underground?

a Cobblestone
b Bedrock
c Granite

10 Glowstone spawns naturally in only which place?

a Basalt Deltas
b Plains
c The Nether

Answers on PAGE 44

MINING – WHAT TO PACK

You need to get packed up for a mining adventure!
Tick the eight most useful items.

☐ compass	☐ arrow	✓ egg	☐ crafting table
☐ flowers	✓ potion	☐ pickaxe	✓ potato
☐ fruit	✓ torch	✓ flower pot	✓ bow
✓ boat	☐ blocks	✓ cooked food	✓ sword

Now put a cross against the four LEAST useful!

GRID GAME

Answers on PAGE 44

Look carefully at the grid below and work out what goes in the missing squares. No item can be repeated in any row or column.

Draw the right item in each square!

SHOW OFF YOUR SHELTER!

Do you ever get stuck for shelter ideas?
You could just have a house of course, but take a look at
the suggestions below for some inspiration for other builds.
Use the grid opposite to plan it and work out what you need.

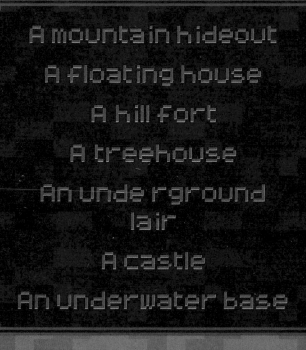

A mountain hideout
A floating house
A hill fort
A treehouse
An underground lair
A castle
An underwater base

YOU MAY WANT YOUR HOME TO HAVE:

STORAGE SPACE

AN ENTRANCE TO YOUR MINE

ROOM FOR YOUR BED

A CRAFTING AREA

A SMELTING AREA

A FARM FOR FOOD

SPACE TO BREW POTIONS

AN ENCHANTING AREA

HOME SWEET HOME

DID YOU KNOW?
HOSTILE CREATURES

Skeletons sink in water. They cannot swim ... but be warned. They do not drown.

A creeper could never hurt a cat - they are scared of them.

Guardians are hostile fish that will always spawn in or around ocean monuments.

YUK FACT: IF YOU KILL A SLIME IT WILL JUST MULTIPLY AND YOU'LL BE IN EVEN MORE TROUBLE!

If you manage to tame a spider, you'll need a saddle to ride it!

SLIMES SPAWN MOSTLY DURING A FULL MOON.

WHICH TOOL?

Work out which tool would be best for each of these jobs. Now draw it in the box.

MINING ORES

TURNING GRASS BLOCKS INTO FARMLAND

COLLECTING WOOD

DIGGING SAND AND DIRT

QUICK QUIZ >>>>>>>

There is only ONE tool that can be used for mining obsidian. What is it?

Shovel

Hoe

Pickaxe

Axe

Diamond pickaxe

18

Answers on PAGE 44

TOP THREE

There is so much to do in Minecraft.
Write down your top three in the categories below:

TOOLS:

....

....

....

WEAPONS:

....

....

....

PETS:

....

....

....

ORES TO MINE:

....

....

....

BIOMES TO LIVE IN

....

....

....

MATES TO GAME WITH

....

....

....

ORE SEARCH

Can you fit the names of eight different ores into this grid?

The first one has been added to help you.

COPPER

LAPIS

COAL

REDSTONE

IRON

GOLD

EMERALD

DIAMOND

LAUGH YOUR BLOCKS OFF!

Here are some great gags to entertain your friends!

HA HA

MY FRIEND WAS MINING WITH A PICKAXE.
Luckily his injuries were . . . minor.

HOW DO YOU CUT DOWN A TREE IN MINECRAFT?
How WOOD I know?

HOW DO CRAFTERS AVOID SUNBURN?
Sunblock

WHAT DO YOU GET IF YOU SPAWN A LOT OF KITTENS?
A meowtain!

LOL!

LOL!

BOOM

WHY COULDN'T THE VILLAGER BREAK THE BEDROCK?
It was just too hard.

WHAT'S SO GOOD ABOUT COBBLESTONE?
It's hand-PICKED!

WHAT DID THE VILLAGER SAY WHEN HE GOT BACK FROM THE CAVE?
It was ore-ful!

MINING MYSTERY

Dig deep and find all the words in this massive grid.

Answers on PAGE 44

Word list:

- ORE
- DIAMOND
- EMERALD
- PICKAXE
- TRIDENT
- CAVE
- TORCH
- GRAVEL
- LAVA
- REDSTONE
- BEDROCK
- GOLD
- LAPIS
- SHOVEL
- CHEST
- LADDER
- BUCKET
- FOOD
- WOOD
- SWORD
- BOW
- ARROWS
- NETHER

Grid:

E	X	A	K	C	I	P	E	J	Q	Z	E
P	R	H	J	O	W	C	M	R	H	V	U
U	A	T	R	O	N	B	E	B	A	J	I
P	P	L	A	G	R	I	R	C	S	V	O
D	I	A	M	O	N	D	A	E	U	O	I
R	E	H	T	E	N	K	L	O	R	V	R
C	T	Y	I	E	D	E	D	T	Y	G	L
K	A	Q	Y	B	L	U	H	G	C	D	H
R	C	B	F	S	N	T	J	Q	D	R	L
P	K	O	I	M	H	P	B	F	T	A	X
T	Q	I	R	V	N	V	Z	A	L	B	F
P	F	D	R	D	A	X	Z	S	A	Q	S
B	A	B	J	T	E	W	Z	R	S	F	G
R	V	B	P	Z	X	B	R	O	E	D	Y
Q	W	X	G	X	K	O	D	K	W	J	Q
V	Q	B	W	F	W	K	S	O	K	V	W
W	O	O	D	S	N	O	M	S	O	N	P
Z	W	W	Y	J	L	B	V	L	M	X	K

G	O	S	V	D	U	Y	H	W	B	C	S	K	G	X	C	Y	J
R	K	H	M	E	H	O	C	B	K	B	V	O	Z	P	C	V	V
A	D	O	S	V	I	H	M	R	E	E	N	O	T	S	D	E	R
V	O	V	I	W	E	N	K	R	D	C	B	M	U	G	L	H	X
E	J	E	K	S	O	B	O	L	G	F	L	W	V	B	D	B	O
L	Z	L	T	X	P	R	O	T	A	I	K	E	O	O	N	S	
I	M	F	U	H	O	G	D	D	N	N	E	N	D	W	E	F	I
L	A	P	I	S	H	W	V	N	E	E	U	Z	L	S	I	U	X
F	Y	F	M	R	O	M	L	P	D	B	D	M	M	A	I	D	M
H	V	V	S	D	K	G	U	K	O	W	L	I	R	H	D	G	Z
Q	E	O	B	B	E	O	R	P	O	M	V	W	R	O	Z	A	Y
U	L	M	D	X	T	H	N	C	S	M	N	D	O	T	K	G	B
T	A	L	I	V	C	C	T	U	L	Z	A	F	I	M	K	D	W
E	D	Q	T	J	N	C	D	E	T	F	T	Z	G	C	W	C	W
O	D	V	K	K	X	D	N	P	K	O	M	F	B	L	U	S	C
A	E	P	G	S	W	J	G	G	A	C	O	T	A	H	B	S	F
X	R	E	K	F	P	C	P	L	Z	T	U	V	Q	R	R	A	V
H	I	B	J	T	M	T	O	R	C	H	A	B	Z	U	P	F	G

TOP TIPS >>>>>>>>>>>>>>>>>

Search left, right, up, down, diagonally, forwards and backwards.

No words are split across both pages.

RUN AROUND THE BLOCK

It's great to be a speedy gamer,
but what about running for real?
Take this challenge to check your pace.

YOU WILL NEED:

A space big enough to
run around, either inside
or outside.

WHAT TO DO:

Make a square using coats, sticks or anything
else you can find to mark the corners.
Each side should be at least 15 strides long.

Choose one corner to be the start.

1 Run forwards to the first corner and STOP.

2 Side step to the next corner and STOP.

3 Hop towards the next corner and STOP.

4 Run forwards to where you started.

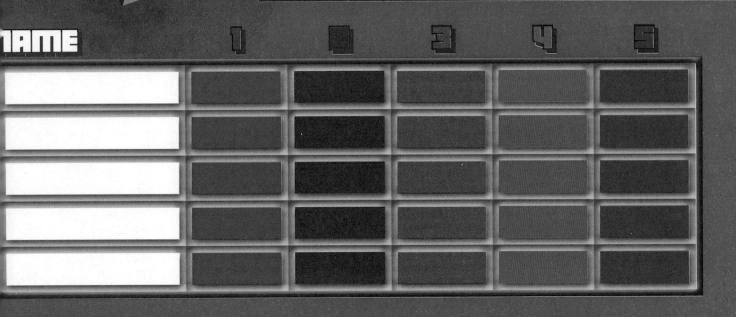

Ask a friend to time you!

warning: You need to stay on your feet so make sure there's nothing in the way to trip over!

Complete the course five times and record the time it takes you here. Which is your fastest lap? Record your friends' times as well.

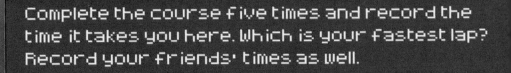

NAME	1	2	3	4	5

♥♥♥ GAIN EXTRA HEALTH POINTS BY:

- ■ Turning around and going the other way

- ■ Doing it all backwards

- ■ Making the square larger

27

JOURNEY TO THE END

Make your way from grassland, through mines to The End and stay away from the baddies.

START

THE END

ALL ABOUT BIOMES

There are over 60 biomes to discover in the game. That's a lot! How many have you ventured into? Let's break down the main biomes you can find.

There are five main types of biomes. Within these are variations and even sub variations. Let's explore a few of them.

LUSH:

PLAINS:

Iconic grass blocks. Low hills. Not many trees or flowers. Watch out for cave openings in the ground. Lava pools are often found here. You'll be able to get yourself a horse, yee-hah!

JUNGLE:

Amazing tall redwood trees grow here, but the vegetation is dense and hard work, as are the hostiles. If you have the stamina they are a great resource for useful items. Cocoa beans to make cookies are a favourite. Also look out for ocelots – you can tame them.

SNOWY:

ICE PLAINS:

Flat and covered in ice and snow – water freezes here instantly! You might be lucky enough to spot a roaming polar bear. Igloos can be found here and most contain loot.

EXTREME HILLS:

Dramatic hills rise up from the ground in this cold biome that can flit between snow and rain. Climb to the top of the hills for amazing views into the distance – just don't fall! You'll love the llamas that spawn here, but not so much the silverfish.

DRY:

DESERT:

Full of sand and cacti and not much else – this is a very hard place to survive. Look out for villages, wells and temples. Some temples can even be found beneath the sand – so keep a look out for clues to lots of lovely loot.

SAVANNAH:

Very dry with no rainfall and lots of flat land. Here you'll find the odd village. Lots of horses and llamas roam the open space too.

OCEAN:

OCEAN AND DEEP OCEAN:

The ocean biomes make up 60% of the game's surface. Get around by swimming or building your very own boat. There is lots of food here and plenty to find and explore, including shipwrecks, temple ruins and buried treasure. Just watch out for hostiles who can pack a real punch, especially if they are armed with a trident.

DEEPER AND DEEPER

How will you make your way to the bottom of this huge cave? Be careful as you dig your way through – just in case there are creatures around corners.

START

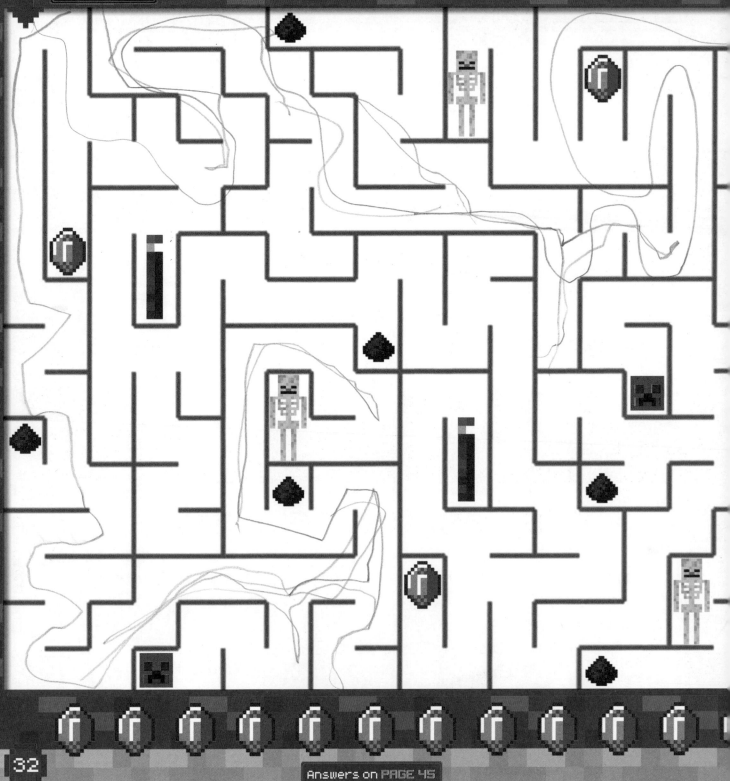

Answers on PAGE 45

Pick up three emeralds and two torches along the way!

FINISH

MASTER BUILDERS

There are lots of things to remember when you are constructing. Follow these tips to make sure that your buildings are the best.

IF YOU'VE JUST STARTED, THINK SMALL. DON'T TRY TO BUILD A MANSION WITH A MOAT BEFORE NIGHTFALL!

BUILD WITH OBSIDIAN AS IT CAN'T BE DESTROYED EASILY.

Use a night-activating lava trap to defend your home.

BOOM BOOM

KEEP A CHEST BY YOUR DOOR, SO YOU CAN GATHER UP ESSENTIALS BEFORE HEADING OUT.

Keep your bed in a secure bunker in the centre of your home so a mob cannot prevent you from sleeping or blow up your bed.

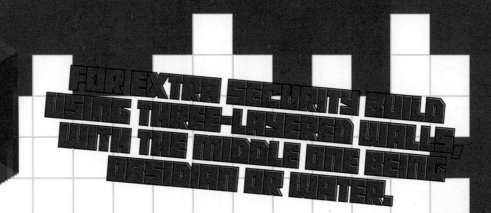

FOR EXTRA SECURITY BUILD
USING THREE-LAYERED WALLS,
WITH THE MIDDLE ONE BEING
OBSIDIAN OR WATER.

Make a good plan,
maybe on paper,
before you start.
Planning is everything.

Make use of different
textures. A white wall can
look special by using bone
blocks, white wool and
quartz mixed up.

CHOOSE YOUR COLOURS
CAREFULLY SO IT ALL
BLENDS WELL TOGETHER.

PROVIDE MOOD
LIGHTING IN YOUR
HOME USING
ICE OR WATER
BLOCKS.

TESTING TIMES

Become better at the game by setting challenges to help you improve. Try and complete each challenge card and log your results below.

Ask an adult to cut out the cards along the dotted lines, shuffle the deck and randomly pick a challenge to attempt!

	Difficulty rating	Time taken	Attempts made
1			
2			
3			
4			
5			
6			
7			
8			
9			

STAY SAFE TIP >>>>>>>>>>>>>>>>>>>>>>>>>>>>>>>

Mine carefully to avoid falling sand and gravel, and watch out for flowing lava when digging upwards.

1 MASTER BUILDER

Build a replica of your own home

2 PARTY TIME!

Make a cake

3 ROYAL COMMAND

Design a castle, with a moat and drawbridge

4 FRIEND ZONE

Get three pets

5 LOADS OF LAYERS

Make a house that has five floors

6 'SHROOM SEARCH

Find a mushroom biome

7 JEWEL DUEL

Be the first to mine a diamond on multiplayer mode

8 PROTECTION SECTION

Get a full set of every type of armour

9 END GAME

Defeat the Ender Dragon

LOOT AND TREASURE GUIDE

MINE FOR DIAMONDS AT Y-LEVEL 11.

That's deep enough for diamonds, but not so deep you risk mining into a lava pool.

CHALLENGE CARD

MINECRAFTERS UNITE

100% UNOFFICIAL

CHALLENGE CARD

MINECRAFTERS UNITE

100% UNOFFICIAL

CHALLENGE CARD

MINECRAFTERS UNITE

100% UNOFFICIAL

CHALLENGE CARD

MINECRAFTERS UNITE

100% UNOFFICIAL

CHALLENGE CARD

MINECRAFTERS UNITE

100% UNOFFICIAL

CHALLENGE CARD

MINECRAFTERS UNITE

100% UNOFFICIAL

CHALLENGE CARD

MINECRAFTERS UNITE

100% UNOFFICIAL

CHALLENGE CARD

MINECRAFTERS UNITE

100% UNOFFICIAL

CHALLENGE CARD

MINECRAFTERS UNITE

100% UNOFFICIAL

DID YOU KNOW? Gold is one of the rarest ores, but it creates the weakest tools.

MIXED UP MUSHROOMS

If you think all these mushrooms are the same, look again! There is ONE that is different to all the others. Circle it if you can find it!

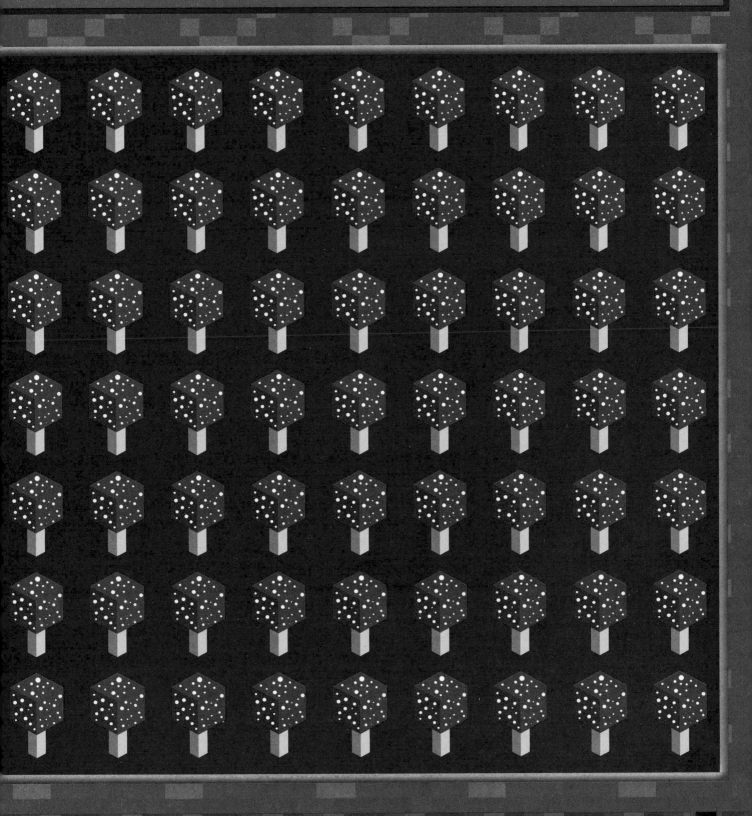

MONSTER MASH-UP

How good are your spotting skills? Look really closely at
the picture and count the correct number of items listed.
Tick the boxes as you find them!

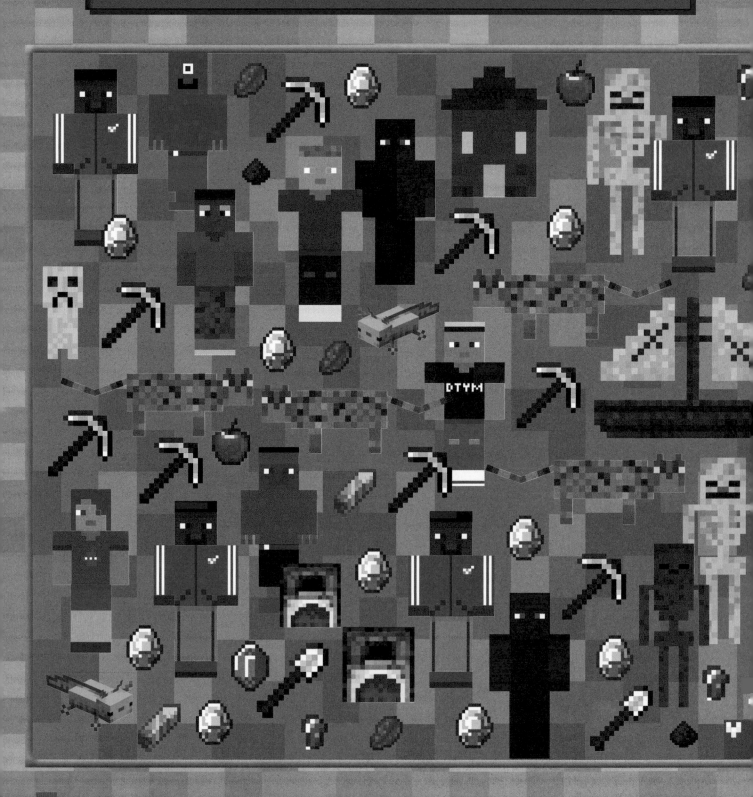

6 ocelots

3 axolotls

5 villagers in blue tops

2 villagers in red tops

1 creeper

4 Endermen

2 skeletons

11 pickaxes

3 shovels

15 diamonds

1 emerald

4 furnaces

DID YOU KNOW?
PASSIVE CREATURES

IF YOU'RE HOLDING WHEAT, MOST FARM ANIMALS WILL FOLLOW YOU, BUT PIGS AND RABBITS NEED CARROTS TO BE TEMPTED!

You can change the colour of your dog's collar using special dyes.

CATS, CHICKENS AND COWS CAN BE KEPT AS PETS TOO!

You can easily tame a wolf with bones to become your pet dog. BUT if you want a cat, you need to feed an ocelot some fish - and this is much harder as they are so shy.

You can make friends with a pig, then craft a carrot on a stick to control it while you ride it around. Yee-hah!

HORSES CAN BE PROTECTED FROM MOBS BY CRAFTING SPECIAL ARMOUR.

ANSWERS

PAGE 10-11:

1. b 2. c
3. c 4. b
5. c 6. c
7. b 8. a
9. b 10. c

PAGE 13:

PAGE 18:

TURNING GRASS BLOCKS INTO FARMLAND	COLLECTING WOOD
DIGGING SAND AND DIRT	MINING ORES
QUICK QUIZ	

PAGE 20:

(Crossword)
GOLD
COPPER
LAPIS
EMERALD
COAL
REDSTONE
DIAMOND
IRON

PAGE 24-25:

(Word search)

ANSWERS

PAGE 28-29:

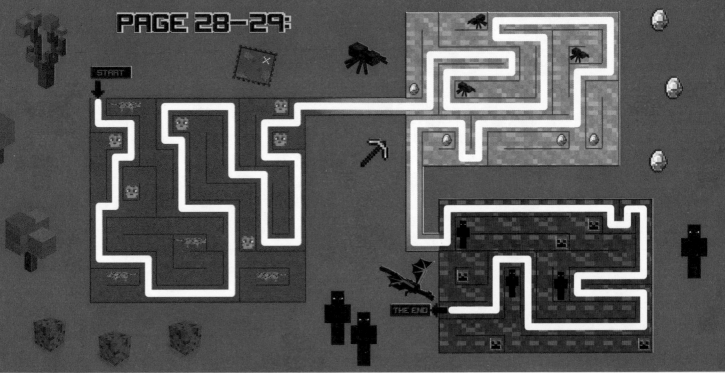

PAGE 32-33:

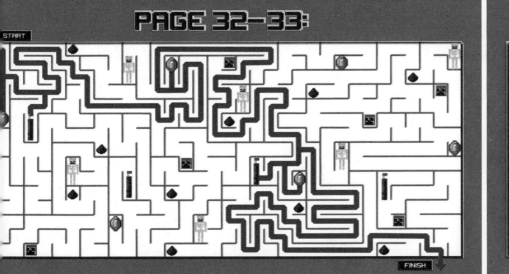

PAGE 39:

PAGE 40-41:

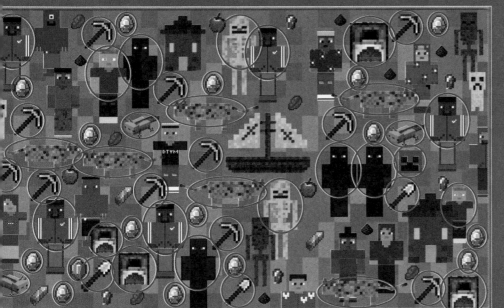
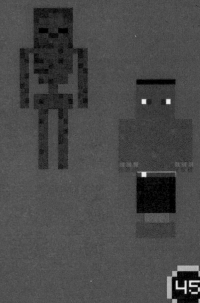